# THE PONY CART ADVENTURE

A True Story

## By Elva Hurst

# THE PONY CART ADVENTURE

## Farm Life Series No. 1

ISBN 978-0-9815205-0-6

Printed in the USA

First Printing, 2008

Publishing Services By:

PUBLISHING and BINDERY

510 Sleepy Hollow Road, Lititz, PA  17543 • (717) 627-3090

For, the "Gang" at Shady Lane Farm

# CONTENTS

# SUMMER PLANS

On the first day of summer vacation the year I was eleven, I woke to the sound of my Father's voice calling up the stairs, "Elva, ziet fer milcha." (Time to milk.)

It's 5:00 in the morning and time to milk the cows again. It was always a little hard to get up so early, but once I was in the cow stable I was glad to be there.

I enjoyed this time of day when the sun

was just beginning to rise over the horizon, birds were singing and, of course, the roosters crowing. In the barn the cows quietly munched on their breakfast of grain and hay while we milked them. My job was to prepare each cow for the automatic milker by washing off her udder with warm soapy water. I had a few minutes before it was time to change the milkers. This was a good time to stand by the back barn door and look out over the meadow and enjoy the view of the creek.

The morning breeze carried the scent of wild flowers and the smells of the creek. Barn swallows flew low and swift through the barn door to their nests they built in the low ceiling of the cow stable. This was the time that I could think, plan, and dream until . . . "Elva, wash off cows number 8, 10, and 12," called my Dad. I washed the cows and then walked back to my thinking spot and ducked my

head as another barn swallow swooped by me carrying in its beak bits of grass and mud from the creek bank.

I felt like these birds were just a nuisance, but Dad said that they were good for the farm because they ate the flies that bothered the cows and the insects in the fields that spoiled the crops. Dad told me that when he was a boy Grandpa said to never destroy a barn swallows nest. If he did, the barn would burn down! While I knew that was superstition, I did learn the value of a barn swallow and ducked once more as the bird flew back out the door.

*"Linda and I have plans today,"* I thought. While walking home from school yesterday

we thought of a grand idea for an

on our first day of summer vacation. *"I do hope*
*Mother approves. What if she says no!"* Finally
the milking was done but I still have to feed
the cats and calves. With a bucket of milk in
each hand I headed to the calf barn to feed the
calves.

This is the last barn chore of the morning
milking, and it won't take me long. *"After that*
*I'll go to the house and tell mom about our plans,"* I
thought. Then suddenly my mental planning
was interrupted by a scurrying, scraping sound
coming from behind me. Before I could turn
to see what it was, I felt a clawing, scratching,
and flopping hit me in the back of the leg!

"Owie, ohh, ouch! You nasty "little" red rooster!" I cried. As I dropped the bucket, milk splashed in every direction, but mostly on my dress! Tears stung my eyes. I whirled around, flinging the other bucket of milk I aimed at the rooster. But he just gracefully stepped aside and the bucket sailed past him, crashing to the ground! "There goes the calves' milk!" I wailed.

I felt like crying. I picked up a now empty bucket and threw it at him again. This time he ran and ducked under the barnyard fence. "That rooster is soooo mean!" I thought. He always attacks when I'm not expecting it!

"Oh dear, now my dress is all wet!" Changing clothes in the middle of my chores will take too long," I decided determinedly. I picked up the empty buckets and headed back to the milk house.

*"This is not good,"* I thought. *"Of all mornings, he had to choose this morning to pick a fight. I'll get even with that rooster, I will! Someday I'll sneak up*

*on him and scare him silly! No! Better yet I'll give him a clobbering he will never forget!"* I refilled the bucket, grabbed the pitchfork for self-defense, and headed back to the calf barn. It was quite a struggle, trying to carry two buckets and a pitchfork. *"This time I am ready for you,"* I

schemed, looking around for the "little" red rooster.

"Why do we call him that anyway?" I wondered. He sure didn't seem little when he floddered me! I watched for him as I walked back to the calf barn but he was nowhere in sight! The mooing sounds of the hungry calves brought my thoughts back to the task of feeding them. They slurped their milk hungrily and wagged their tails as if to say, "Thank you."

Finally I headed to the house. As I was coming up the walk I could smell breakfast cooking. "It smells like fried mush and puddin's this morning! Yum! Probably fried mush with Uncle Norman's puddin's on top. What a breakfast treat!" My mouth watered.

I washed up for breakfast and got out of my smelly barn clothes. "Now, I'm going to ask mother about meeting Linda and going on that adventure! But where is she?" I checked upstairs—she wasn't there. Next I checked the cellar but she wasn't there either! Where was she anyway!? Finally I found her in the garden, picking sugar peas.

I took a deep breath and told her all about our plans. Without hesitating she responded, "After all these sugar peas are picked, you can go!"

*"That means yes!"* I thought. But more work!

I picked sugar peas as fast as I could. *"I sure hope she doesn't make me clean them too!"* I thought.

# MORE WORK

I finished picking peas in a hurry, got on my bike, and rode toward Linda's house. Though Linda was younger than me, I liked being with her. She was wise and sensible. She thought before she spoke and considered the consequences before doing something. Linda was the oldest in her family and a very good big sister to her seven brothers and sisters.

Their farm was at the end of a very long

lane. Many horses grazed in the pasture next to the lane. I liked to hear them whinny. They were big, strong Belgium workhorses. They were very important to Linda's family because her Father used these horses to work in the field. My dad used a tractor.

Linda's family was Old Order Mennonite. They did not use a car for transportation. They used a horse and buggy instead. The horses used to pull the buggy were tall, slender, swift horses that didn't mind the noise of the traffic on the road. As I drew closer to the farmhouse I could hear the sounds of children playing in the yard and the geese honking in the orchard.

I found Linda in the barn, taking care of Nancy, her family's blue-eyed chestnut-colored pony.

"Good morning, Linda," I called. "What did your mom say? Are you allowed to go?" Linda hesitated. "Well, what did she say?" I asked.

"I didn't ask her yet," she replied.

"I'll get water for Nancy while you go to the house and ask," I suggested.

I led Nancy to the watering trough at the forebay of the barn. As I waited for Nancy to finish, I stood by the barn door and watched for Linda.

*"I do hope she's allowed to go,"* I thought as I

waited impatiently. Linda was never in a hurry, not even today! Finally I saw her coming down the walk. I strained to see the expression on her face. "Yes! She's smiling. I'm sure that means good news!" I told myself.

"Mom said I'm allowed to go, but first I have to hang up the wash," she said.

*"Not more work!"* I thought. But instead, I said, "Don't worry. I'll help and, together, we can finish in a hurry."

We lead Nancy back to her stall and gave her some hay to munch. Next we gave hay to Bonnie, the milk cow that was in the stall beside Nancy. When that was done we headed for the wash house—an unheated room next to the kitchen, where they did their laundry. It had a concrete floor that was always wet!

I groaned inwardly at the sight of the piles of laundry we had to hang before we could go. Laundry was all over the wash house floor! The gas motor on the wringer washing machine was loud. Linda's mother took the wet clothes one by one from the washer putting each piece through the two rollers that would squeeze out the excess water. This machine was called a "wringer washer."

Cautiously, she fed the clothes through the wringer, being careful not to get her hands caught between the rollers. As the wash passed through, it came out the other side, flat as a pancake. We would shake it out and then hang it on the line.

Right outside the wash house door was a balcony with a wheel up in the corner that held the clothesline. It stretched all the way across the yard to another wheel by the barn roof. I liked the view from the balcony; from here I could see the horses in the meadow and the ducks on the creek. My eyes followed the lane all the way to my farm across the road.

From here I could even see our clothesline, already full of laundry. For a moment I forgot what I was doing until I heard Linda calling for more clothespins. Together we hung the wash as fast as we could. The first load was

mostly cloth diapers for Linda's baby sister. Diapers, diapers, and more diapers—would we ever finish!

The second load was mostly towels and washclothes. Before long the whole line was full of clothes. The warm sun and a light breeze blowing would dry the wash very quickly.

When we were finished, we looked at each other and said, "Let's go!"

Together we raced across the yard to the barn.

# Our Adventure Begins

We ran to the shed where the pony cart was kept. Linda lifted the shaft while I pushed from behind. Together we pushed and pulled the cart to the area of the barn where the horses were. Nancy's ears perked up at the sound of the harness. Linda got her out of her stall and urged her to back up to the cart. Before long we had her hitched up and ready to go!

Jumping up on the black leather seat, I felt a tingle of excitement. Finally our adventure had begun! I turned to Linda and asked, "Do you have your money?"

"Oh, no! I almost forgot!" she gasped. "Here, hold the reins while I go the house to get it."

*"Okay, please hurry,"* I thought. I didn't have a way with horses like Linda did. *"What if Nancy doesn't listen to me? What if she takes off around the corner and out the lane without Linda?"*

On and on went my imagination as Nancy pawed the ground impatiently. She was ready to be off as soon as possible. I was relieved to see Linda reappear with her money. She hopped up on the seat and flicked the reins. Nancy started forward.

Finally we were off! As we rounded the corner of the driveway my eyes caught sight of something at the other end of the lane. What was it? "Oh, no!" I groaned. The hammer mill truck was making its way slowly up the lane.

Linda called to the pony, "Whoa, Nancy," and pulled back on the reins. Nancy slowed down reluctantly. With a bank on one side of the lane and the meadow fence on the other, we were unable to turn around, so we had to back into the yard until the truck passed.

"Back up," Linda called to Nancy. She obeyed and backed awkwardly into the yard.

We pulled aside just as the noisy machine passed by.

This big truck with a mill on it went from farm to farm ground cobs of corn into fine grain for cattlefeed. As soon as the truck passed by, we were off once more. As we bumped out the lane, we hung on to the small handles at either end of the seat. I thought, "What an exciting ride!"

The horses in the meadow looked up from grazing and watched us go. No doubt they were wishing they could go too! Nancy's hooves made a beautiful clop-clopping sound on the smooth road pavement. The day was perfect for a trip to Joan's Economy Shop—a thrift store that sold used clothes and other items at a nearby town.

Since the store was only three miles away, we could get to it by back roads in thirty minutes if Nancy kept her pace. Together, Linda and I watched for traffic and enjoyed the countryside. Over the bridge we went, past the woods, and then up over the hill and past the school house.

Already our one-room school looked deserted; the swings looked lonely. The neighbor had turned his horse into the playground to keep the grass short over the summer. The rope across the school entrance seemed to call out, "School's closed." We had

turned into that driveway for eight months of the year, now it felt good to ride on by. Linda and I looked at each other and whooped, "Yahoo!"

# FINDING TREASURES

With the wind in my face and the school behind my back, I felt happy! Happy and thankful for the summer vacation and for my friend Linda, and, of course, Nancy, who was giving us such a fine ride! I turned to Linda and asked, "How much money were you able to save?"

Keeping her eyes on the road she answered, "Three dollars."

*"I have four dollars,"* I thought. *"I'll share fifty cents with her. Then we will both have three dollars and fifty cents to spend on whatever we want!"*

I could hardly wait to get to the store. By now we had driven nearly half way. The ride was good so far. No noisy motorcycles or loud cars had spooked Nancy. We were getting closer to town, and traffic was increasing.

"Linda is such a good driver," I mused. She pulled on the right rein. Nancy obeyed and turned into the next road without slowing her pace. We were almost there. We had only one long hill to go. Now I could see the sign by the road: Joan's Economy Shop.

We turned into the driveway. Linda pulled Nancy in the shade of the tree by the hitching post. Linda took the lead rope from under the

seat and snapped it onto Nancy's halter and tied it securely to the ring on the hitching post. She patted her pony on the back and turned to the store.

I felt for the money in my pocket. *"What if it fell out during our long ride?"* I worried as I felt for the dollar bills. *"They were there! It's a good thing Mother sews our pockets deep!"* I thought. The sign on the door read "Open" with the stores hours listed beneath it. When we opened the door the familiar bell jingled overhead. Joan greeted us with a warm smile.

She knew us well because our families did most of their shopping here for clothes and shoes. Rarely ever did we buy store-bought clothes brand new. We usually wore hand-me-downs. On rare occasions, Mother sewed a new Sunday dress just for me!

The first aisle had men's clothing; the second had ladies' clothing. I wanted to see things in the third aisle. It had rows and rows of books on one side and toys on the other side. I loved to read. Every time I came I'd check to see if any new books had come in since I was here last. I tried my best to pick out decent books by reading titles and the back cover first, because Mother wanted us to buy decent books.

I pulled *The Secret Raft* off the shelf. That sounded good. The picture on the cover showed children about my age drifting through an eerie swamp on a homemade raft.

I turned to show it to Linda, but she wasn't there! Where was she anyway? I looked in the next aisle, but she wasn't there. Finally I found her in the back room, looking at shoes for her brother.

To help her find the right size, her mother had traced her brother's foot on a piece of brown paper and cut it out for a pattern. Then at the store Linda could just hold the pattern to the sole of the shoes to get the right size.

I showed Linda my book and helped her to shop. There were shoes of all kinds of styles and colors. But we were only allowed to wear black shoes. This made our job easier. We picked out a few black shoes and held the pattern to the sole of a pair of shoes that looked good enough for Sunday. Satisfied with her choice, Linda was ready to shop for herself.

As we entered the next room beyond the shoes, we spied rows and rows of pretty pins hanging from a cloth on the door—pretty, shiny, glittery pins of all designs. We were not allowed to wear other kinds of jewelry, but we were allowed to wear decorative pins on our coats and sweaters, so we decided to each pick one. I choose a pretty Christmas bell; I would save it to wear at Christmastime. Linda picked out a flower that glittered yellow in the center.

Mentally, I tried to figure up the bill because I didn't want to get to the checkout counter and not have enough of money. That would be embarrassing! Best I could figure I had a little money left to spend, so we looked at the scarves and sweaters. After that we went back to the toy shelf. I wanted to find something for my little brother. At the checkout counter I discovered I had made out pretty good. I had fifty cents left over!

# An
# Unexpected End

We had shopped for more than an hour. I hoped Nancy didn't mind waiting that long! We said goodbye to Joan and went out the door. Outside, something didn't seem right. It was too dark for the middle of the afternoon! I glanced at the sky and called to Linda, "A storm is coming!" Overhead dark clouds dotted the sky. Nancy sensed the coming storm and pulled at her rope and pawed the ground. She wanted to get home!

I stuffed our bag of treasures under the seat while Linda hurried to untie Nancy. The pony backed up and turned to go just as Linda jumped on the seat. I checked the sky again to see if I could tell which direction the storm was headed, but it was hard to tell. The sky seemed bluish-gray all over!

Nancy knew which way was home and turned left at the road without having to be told where to go. Thunder rumbled in the distance and lightning flashed across the horizon. We had not figured a storm into our

adventure, but we were caught in it whether we liked it or not!

Hopefully we would make it back to the house before the worst of it got here. My thoughts went in all directions. Though I have never seen a tornado I had heard that tornadoes had winds so strong they could blow down houses and trees. My stomach tightened at the thought of such a storm. What would we do!

I looked at Linda; she was busy with the reins, trying to keep Nancy from going down the hill too fast. The pony cart bobbed up and down as Nancy's hooves flew over the pavement. Her mane and tail flowed in the wind. She was doing her best to get us home in a hurry.

She wanted to be home just as much as we did. We were almost halfway now. I could see the schoolhouse up ahead. The sky was getting darker. Big raindrops began to fall slowly at first, blurring my glasses and making it difficult to see the road.

I checked the bags under the seat. I stuffed Linda's paper bag into my plastic bag, hoping to keep our treasures safe and dry. Now the thunderclaps came closer and closer together, followed by bright flashes of lightning. "Hurry, hurry," my heart seemed to cry with every beat.

Linda called to me over the noise of the storm and Nancy's hooves. "Let's take a shortcut through Bucher's field lane," she shouted.

"Okay, sounds good," I yelled back. A shortcut sounded wise to me. The rain was pouring down hard. We could barely see the road. Linda turned Nancy into the edge of the field, without slowing down.

"Hang on!" Linda yelled, looking scared but determined. We awkwardly bumped our way across the field. The rain was coming down hard and fast! Little streams of water began to rise in the ruts of the field lane. The pony cart wheels slid around stones and rocks.

In my heart I began to pray, *"Dear Lord,*

*help us to get home safely!"* I couldn't see a thing!
But Nancy kept right on going as if she could
see just fine.

My bare feet could feel the water rising
in the bottom of the cart. *"Oh no, at this rate
The Secret Raft book would surely float away!"* I
thought as I felt for the bag with my feet. I
couldn't let go of the handlebars to hold the
bag, so I pinched it between my legs.

The pony cart lurched back and forth and
bounced over more rocks and potholes now
filled with water. The wheels sprayed water up
the sides. *"Poor Nancy,"* I thought, *"she must be
tired."* But on and on she pulled us.

Suddenly, out of the darkness of the storm,

I saw the barn rise on our left. We had made it! Nancy had found her way in the storm through the neighbor's field and all the way to Linda's barn! She didn't slow down until she had pulled us to safety under the forebay of the barn.

There, we felt much safer. We were soaked from head to toe—soaked but safe!

Nancy just stood there, her sides heaving as her breaths came in big huffs and puffs. She was dripping with rain and sweat. Foam had gathered by the bit in her mouth. Quickly we hurried to unhitch her from the cart, pulled off her bridle, and rubbed her to help her cool down.

"Good girl, good girl," Linda kept saying. I could see she was proud of her pony. Finally, we lead her to the watering trough, where she gratefully took a long drink!

Suddenly the barn door burst open with a bang! Someone entered with a coat draped over his head. It was Linda's dad. He looked relieved to see us safe in the barn!

I continued to brush Nancy as Linda told her dad all about the shortcut and how Nancy got us home when we couldn't see where we were going!

We led Nancy to her stall and treated her to some more grain and hay. Suddenly I remembered our shopping bags in the pony cart. I hurried back to the cart, and lifted out the bag. It was dripping wet!

"Is everything okay?" asked Linda, as she joined me beside the cart.

Together we sat on a bale of hay. I handed the paper bag to Linda and then reached into my plastic bag. I was mostly concerned about the book. But, sure enough, it was dry. What a relief! *The Secret Raft* didn't even get wet! I reached into the bag for the pin and my brother's toy—they were all there, safe and dry.

I turned to Linda and asked, "Are your things okay?" She assured me they were. Together we sat on the hay and waited for the rain to slow down before we walked to the house. Now the thunder sounded very far in the distance. We talked about our trip to the thrift shop, the treasures we had found, and how brave Nancy was in the storm. We were tired and hungry but very happy. Then I realized that I had asked God for help in our time of trouble but had never thanked Him. Quietly in my heart I thanked Him for helping us get back home safely.

Then I turned to Linda and asked, "Shall we do it again sometime?"

Lifting an eyebrow, she turned to me and answered, "Well, maybe."

# GLOSSARY

**Barnyard**

A fenced-in area next to the barn where the animals are kept

**Cloth Diapers**

Washable diapers made of cotton cloth; used instead of expensive disposable diapers

**Floddered**

It's when a rooster runs into you, flapping his wings, scratching with his claws, and pecking at you. Ouch!

**Field lane**

A dirt road that cut through the field from the road to the back of the barn; used to get from field to field with farm equipment

## Forebay

An area in the front of the barn that overhangs the edge of the barnyard and is separated from the animal stalls by a wall; area where horses are watered, harnessed, and shoed

## Hand-me-downs

Clothes that older brothers and sisters had worn or outgrown and were kept for the next younger ones in line

## Hitching post

A post with a metal ring attached to it where the lead rope from the horse's bridle was snapped onto the ring, holding the horse in place

## Mennonite

A group of Christians named after their Anabaptist leader, Menno Simons (1456-1561); his teaching emphasized non-violence, community, and service. Mennonites today still seek a plain and simple lifestyle, separate from the world and its dangerous influences

## Mush

A cereal made of corn meal. The corn meal is boiled in water and salt then cooked, sliced, and fried in lard.
(See recipe following glossary)

## Old Order Mennonite

A branch of the Mennonite church whose lifestyle is similar to the Amish in tradition and transportation. They use the horse and buggy instead of vehicles

## One room school

A school building that has only one classroom where all eight grades are educated

## Puddin's

A meat pudding made from meat scraped from the bone. This meat and the bone are boiled together in water with spices; then separated and drained. The meat is ground fine and served over fried mush

## Tornado

A violent storm with very strong winds, forming a funnel-shaped cloud that reaches to the ground and destroys many things in its path

## Wringer washing machine

An old-fashioned clothes washing machine that had two wooden rollers that squeeze out excess water as the clothes pass through

# RECIPES

### Corn Meal Mush

Bring 2 1/2 cups of water and 1 tsp. of salt to a boil, meanwhile, mix 1 cup of corn meal (I buy the roasted corn meal) with 1 cup of cold water. Add this mixture to the hot water, stirring while pouring. Cook about 15 minutes stirring occasionally to keep it smooth.

This mixture can be served hot with milk and butter, but I like to put it in a loaf pan to cool for several hours or overnight. Then it can be sliced and fried in a hot skillet with olive oil or lard until browned. Some like it with catsup or maple syrup, but I think it's delicious with stewed crackers and eggs!

## Stewed Crackers

Brown 1 tsp. of butter in a small pan, add 1 cup of milk and two handfuls of slightly crushed soda crackers. When thoroughly soaked and heated, pour over fried mush and eggs. Yum!

This kind of breakfast is most delicious after a morning of hard work in the barn on a cold winter morning!

# Also Written and Illustrated by Elva Hurst

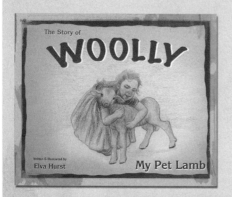

## The Story of Woolly My Pet Lamb

To order books and visit Elva's Barnyard Art Gallery online, go to www.elvaschalkart.com

*You can also write to:*

Barnyard Art
1519 Brunnerville Rd.
Lititz, Pa 17543

Pony and Foal

Elva (14 years old) and her sister posing with Nancy on a Sunday afternoon.

Elva's present day horse Maggie, with her foal Oreo.

A bareback ride on one of the ponies at the farm.